# The new baby

Written by Helen Brain

Illustrated by Jeff Rankin

**NEW READERS PROJECT**

In May my daughter came to me. "Mama," she said, "I'm going to have a baby."

"You're only seventeen," I shouted at her. "How could you be so stupid?"

"What will the people in the church say? What will your father say?"

Her father was very angry. "I am glad my dear mother is not alive to see this," he shouted at her. "She would have been very ashamed."

"You are the child of a priest. You should not have let this happen."

For seven months he would not talk to her. "I want nothing to do with her," he told me. "She has brought shame on our family."

13

Last week my daughter's pains
started. I took her to the hospital.

15

On Monday I fetched her. We came home with the baby. Her father was still angry.

But then I showed him the baby.

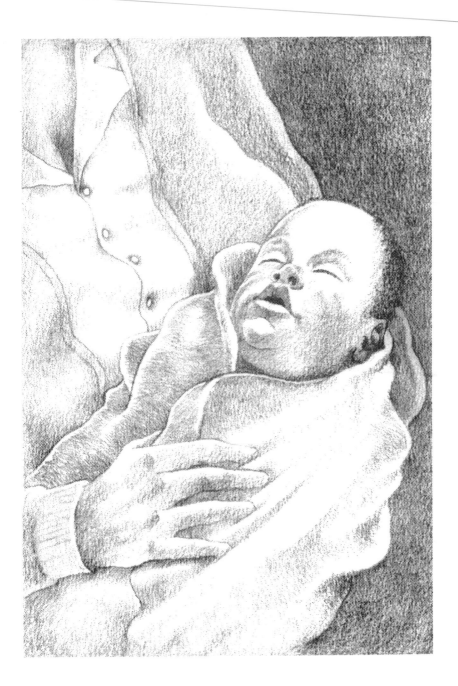

19

He looked at his granddaughter. She opened her eyes and looked at him too.

"Maria," he said to me. His eyes were full of tears. "Maria, this child looks like my dear late mother."

He kissed the baby. Then he kissed our daughter.

"Thanks be to God," he said. "I am a grandfather."

THE END

# Thanks

We thank the following people for their help in evaluating this story:

Jabu Ngiba, Philile Dhlamini, Beatrice Mabaso, Jean Keyser, Rike Sitas, Daniela McCullough, Shelley Seid, Rick Garvey and learners of Chesterville Literacy Project, Pam Mfeka, Zanele Mabaso, Thami Xaba, Bev May and colleagues, Rehana Laher, Fiona Knight and colleagues and learners, Muthande Society for the Aged Literacy Project learners, Chris Ramdas, Norman Mbuthuma, Lawrence Mtuli, Anton Khoza and Mpume Mkhize at Westville Methodist Church Literacy Project.